THE BIGGEST SONGS OF 2002

Exclusive distributors:

c Sales Limited 8/9 Frith Street, London W1D 3JB, England.
mited 120 Rothschild Avenue, Rosebery, NSW 2018, Australia.

Order No. AM975898 ISBN 0-7119-9741-1
This book © Copyright 2002 by Wise Publications

Music arranged by Derek Jones and Jack Long.
Music processed by Paul Ewers Music Design.
Printed and bound in Malta by Interprint Ltd.

www.musicsales.com

D1493085

WISE PUBLICATIONS
London/New York/Sydney/Paris/Copenhagen/Berlin/Madrid/Tokyo

ANYONE OF US (STUPID MISTAKE)

Words & Music by Jörgen Elofsson, Per Magnusson & David Kreuger

1. I've been let-ting you down, down. Girl, I know I've been such a fool.
(Verse 2 see block lyric)

Giv-ing in to temp - ta - tion,_ I should-'ve played it cool.

Verse 2:
She was kind of excited
A little crazy, I should of known
She must have altered my senses
'Cause I offered to walk her home.
The situation got out of hand
I hope you understand.

It can happen to any one of us *etc.*

COLOURBLIND

Words & Music by Darius, Pete Glenister & Denny Lew

1. Feel-in' blue___ ___ when I'm tryin' to for-get the feel-in' that I___ miss___ you.

Verse 2:
Feelin' red
When you spend all your time with your friends
And not me instead.
Feelin' black
When I think about all of the things
That I feel I lack.

Feelin' jaded when it's not gone right,
All the colours have faded.
When I feel your eyes, on me
Feeling fine, sublime
When that smile of yours creeps into my mind.
Mm, mm.

CAUGHT IN THE MIDDLE

Words & Music by Ben Adams, Paul Marazzi, Chris Porter & Rick Mitra

1. You said that love__ was just__ a state__ of_____

mind,_____ a puz - zle made_ of pie - ces you_ can't_____

find._____ But for me you nev - er real - ly had the time_ and

I was_ blind,_____ oh._____

2. And ev - 'ry- thing_ that you meant to me_____
(Verse 3 see block lyric)

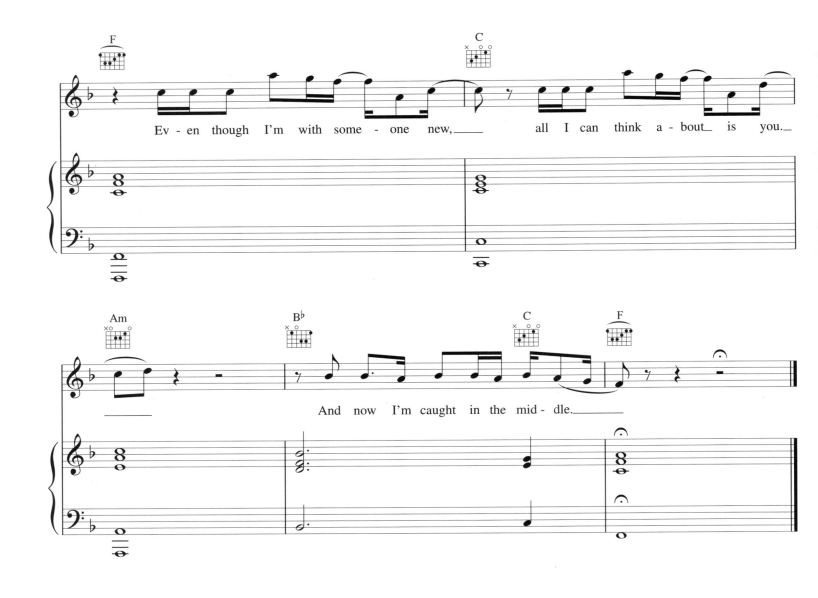

Verse 3:
Moving on, she brings me brighter days
But thoughts of you are in my mind always
Like a memory that I can't erase
It's here to stay

Things are so different   etc.

EVERGREEN

Words & Music by Jörgen Elofsson, Per Magnusson & David Kreuger

Verse 2:
Touch like an angel
Like velvet to my skin
And I wonder
I wonder why you wanna stay the night
What you're dreaming
What's behind.
Don't tell me, but it feels like love.

I'm gonna take this moment *etc.*

FANTASY

Words & Music by Gareth Young & Andrew Hayman

Verse 2:
Do you like what you see?
Do you feel that you're closer to reality?
Boy this isn't a dream
Can you be everything that I want you to be?

I'm better than anyone, anyone you ever had
So come on give up, give in to me
Show me how I drive you mad
How you wanna be, be so bad.

I ain't foolin' around *etc.*

FLY BY II

Words & Music by Mikkel SE, Hallgeir Rustan,
Tor Erik Hermansen, Simon Webbe, Randy Alpert & Herb Alpert

Verse 2:
Girl it's time to let you know
I'm down if you wanna go
We can take it nice and slow
We got until tomorrow
U.K. style U.K. flow
We got you hot like whoah
With the hot stuff - top stuff - yo, we got stuff.

What a night so far *etc.*

FREAK LIKE ME

Words & Music by Gary Numan, Eugene Hanes, Marc Valentine,
Loren Hill, William Collins, George Clinton & Gary Cooper

Verse 2:
Boy you're moving kind of slow
You gotta keep it up now there you go
That's just one thing that a man must do
I'm packing all the flavours you need
I got you shook up on your knees
'Cause it's all about the dog in me.

I wanna freak in the morning   *etc.*

I'M NOT A GIRL, NOT YET A WOMAN

Words & Music by Max Martin, Rami & Dido

that life does-n't al - ways____ go my____ way,

yeah.____ Feels like I'm caught____ in the mid - dle,____

that's when I re - al - ise____ I'm not a girl,____

not yet a wo - man.____ All I

Verse 2:
I'm not a girl
There is no need to protect me
It's time that I, learn to face up to this
On my own
I've seen so much more than you know now
So don't tell me to shut my eyes.

I'm not a girl *etc.*

HERO

Words & Music by Enrique Iglesias, Paul Barry & Mark Taylor

Oh._____ I just wan - na hold you._____

51

Verse 2:
Would you swear that you'll always be mine?
Would you lie? Would you run and hide?
Am I in too deep? Have I lost my mind?
I don't care, you're here tonight.

I can be your hero baby *etc.*

IN MY PLACE

Words & Music by Guy Berryman, Jon Buckland, Will Champion & Chris Martin

1. In my place, in my____ place were lines that I____ could-n't
   (Verse 2 see block lyric)

Verse 2:
I was scared, I was scared
Tired and under-prepared
But I'll wait for it.
And if you go, if you go
It'll leave me down here on my own
Then I'll wait for you, yeah.

Yeah, how long must you wait   *etc.*

JUST A LITTLE

Words & Music by Michelle Escoffery, George Hammond Hagan & John Hammond Hagan

Repeat ad lib. to fade

Verse 2:
Let me, I'd do anything if you just let me
Find a way to make you explore
I know you wanna break down those walls, yeah
And it's so challenging
Getting close to you's what I'm imagining
I just wanna see you get down
You gotta let it all out.

Oh baby won't you work it a little *etc.*

KISS KISS

Words & Music by Aksu Sezen, Juliette Jaimes & Steve Welton-Jaimes

Mm!

Mm!

1. When you look at me, tell me what you see. This is what you get, it's the way I am.
(Verse 2 see block lyric)

Verse 2:
You could be mine baby, what's your star sign
Won't you take a step into the lions den
I can hear my conscience calling me, calling me
Say I'm gonna be a bad girl again
Why don't you come on over, we can't leave this all undone
Got a devil on my shoulder, there's no place for you to run.

You don't have to act   *etc.*

LAZY

Words & Music by David Byrne,
Darren Rock, Ashley Beedle & Darren House

Oh._____

I'm_____ wick - ed an' I'm la - zy._____

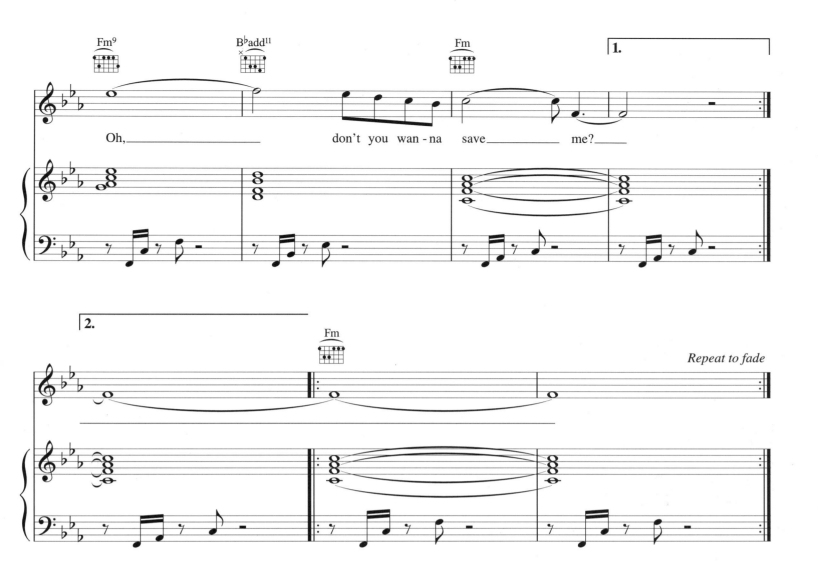

Verse 2:
Well some folks they got money
And some folks lives are sweet
Some folks make decisions
And some folks clean the streets
Now imagine what it feels like
Imagine how it sounds
Imagine life is perfect
And everything works out
No tears are falling from my eyes
I'm keeping all the pain inside
Now don't you wanna live with me
I'm lazy as a man can be.

I'm wicked and I'm lazy   *etc.*

Verse 3:
Imagine there's a girlfriend
Imagine there's a job
Imagine there's an answer
Imagine there's a God
Imagine I'm a devil
Imagine I'm a saint
Lazy money, lazy sexy, lazy out of space
No tears are falling from my eyes
I'm keeping all the pain inside
Now, don't you wanna live with me
I'm lazy as a man can be.

I'm wicked and I'm lazy   *etc.*

THE LONG AND WINDING ROAD

Words & Music by John Lennon & Paul McCartney

Verse 2:
The wild and windy night
That the rain washed away
Has left a pool of tears
Crying for the day
Why leave me standing here?
Let me know the way

Many times I've beeen alone *etc.*

A LITTLE LESS CONVERSATION

Words & Music by Billy Strange & Scott Davis

SOMETHIN' STUPID

Words & Music by C. Carson Parks

then I go and spoil it all__ by say-ing some-thing stu-pid like I love__ you.__

Repeat ad lib. to fade

I love__ you.__   I

Verse 2:
I practise every day to find
Some clever lines to say
To make the meaning come true
But then I think I'll wait until
The evening gets late
And I'm alone with you
The time is right
Your perfume fills my head
The stars get red
And oh, the night's so blue
And then I go and spoil it all
By saying something stupid
Like I love you.

STOP CRYING YOUR HEART OUT

Words & Music by Noel Gallagher

Cos all of the stars Stop cry-ing your heart out.

Stop cry-ing your heart out.

Stop cry-ing your heart

out.

Verse 2:
Get up. Come on
Why you scared?
(I'm not scared)
You'll never change what been and gone.

Cos all of the stars   *etc.*

A THOUSAND MILES

Words & Music by Vanessa Carlton

1. Mak-ing my way down town, walk-ing fast;
(Verse 2 see block lyric)

fac-es pass,_ and I'm home-bound.

Verse 2:
It's always times like these
When I think of you
And I wonder if you ever think of me
'Cause everything's so wrong
And I don't belong
Living in your precious memory
'Cause I need you
And I miss you
And now I wonder:

If I could fall into the sky *etc.*

WHENEVER, WHEREVER

Words by Shakira & Gloria Estefan
Music by Shakira & Tim Mitchell

Verse 2:
Lucky that my lips not only mumble
They spill kisses like a fountain
Lucky that my breasts are small and humble
So you don't confuse them with mountains
Lucky I have strong legs like my mother
To run for cover when I need it
And these two eyes are for no other
The day you leave will cry a river
Le do le le le le, le do le le le le
At your feet, I'm at your feet.

Whenever, wherever   *etc.*

WHEREVER YOU WILL GO

Words & Music by Aaron Kamin & Alex Band

Verse 2:
And maybe I'll find out a way to make it back some day
To want you, to guide you through the darkest of your days
If a great wave shall fall
It'll fall upon us all
Well then I hope there's someone out there
Who can bring me back to you.

If I could then I would *etc.*

YOUR SONG

Words & Music by Elton John & Bernie Taupin

done,___ I hope you don't mind, I hope you don't mind,___

that I put___ down in words how won-der-ful life is while

you're in___ the world.___

Kids. And you can tell ev-'ry-bo-dy this is the

2°:
I sat on the roof and I kicked up the moss
Well a few of the verses, they've got me quite cross
But the sun's been quite kind while I wrote this song
It's for people like you that keep it turned on
So excuse me forgetting that these things I do
Just see I've forgotton if they're green or they're blue
Anyway the thing is what I really mean
Oh, yours are the sweetest eyes I've ever seen.

THE TIDE IS HIGH (GET THE FEELING)

Words & Music by John Holt, Howard Barrett, Tyrone Evans, Bill Padley & Jem Godfrey

Verse 4:
Every girl wants you to be her man
But I'll wait right here till it's my turn
I'm not the kind of girl who gives up just like that
Oh no.